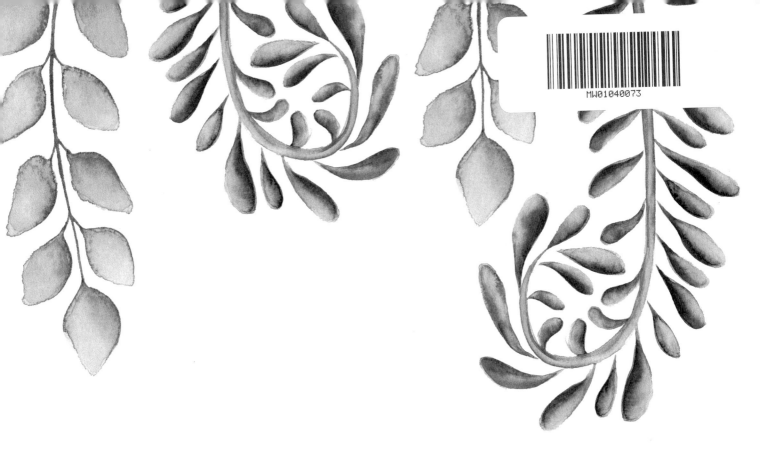

This book belongs to

www.JoAnnMDickinsonAuthor.com

Library of Congress Control Number: 2022908958

ISBN: Hardcover 978-1-7378041-7-8
Paperback 978-1-7378041-8-5

Two Sweet Peas Publishing

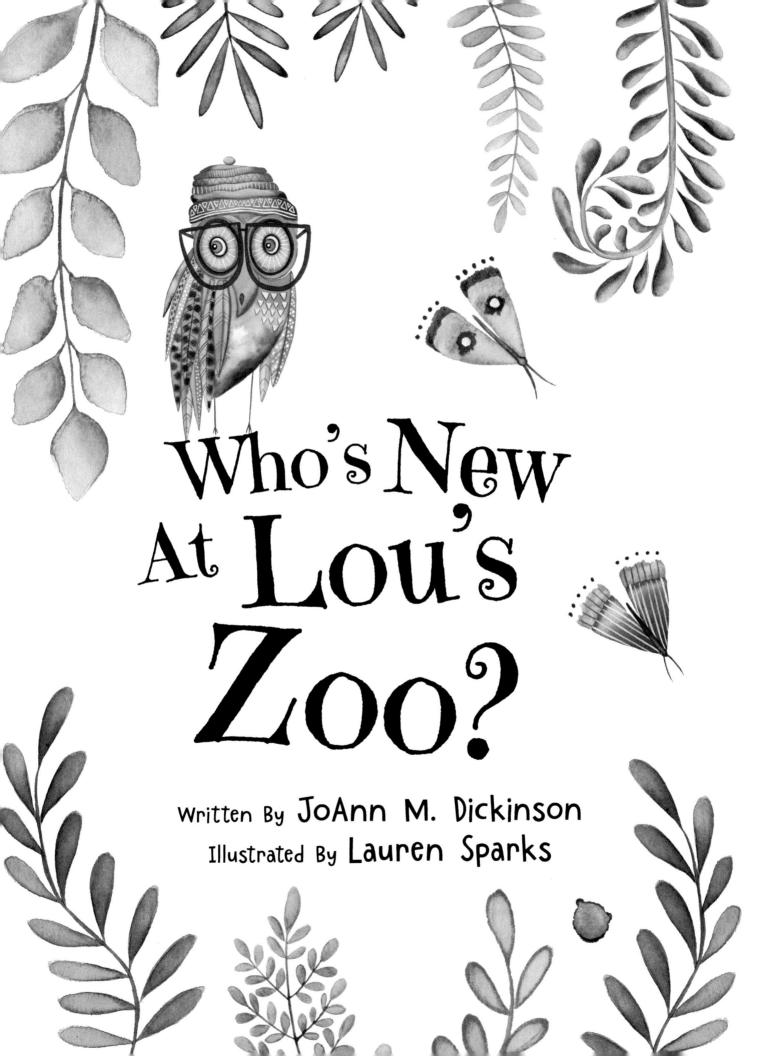

Who's New At Lou's Zoo?

Written By JoAnn M. Dickinson

Illustrated By Lauren Sparks

Hi!

My name is Lou, and I'm an alpaca.
My friends and I live in, something
human's call a "neighborhood."

I have always wanted to be a zookeeper
in my own zoo. And now that
I have so many great friends,
I call our neighborhood my zoo.

In this story, you will meet my wonderful
and loyal friends from many different
places, and you will learn some
fun facts about each of them!

A new guest is coming to
Lou's neighborhood zoo.
Lou and the others are excited to
see who this new guest will be!

"I must start planning a party so everyone can meet each other!" LOU exclaims.

"We want them to feel welcome and accepted by all the animals."

"Who do you think this
mysterious new guest will be?"
Peter, the Chatty Parrot,
asks Gage, the Glorious Gorilla.
"I wonder if they will have
beautiful colors like me. . .
or what they will eat. . .
or what their name is. . .
or where they will stay!"

I'm wondering that too!

Gage tells Peter.

Gage, the Glorious Gorilla, has been at the zoo for many years and he is not interested in discovering who his new neighbor might be. But he *would* like to see if they are young or old like him.

Mickey, the Meek Monkey,

is a bit more curious—trying to guess whether the new guest would be small like him or much larger. Mickey worries that he and the other animals might feel the new guest won't fit into their neighborhood.

Then, Wally, the Loyal Walrus, says, "I would like to know if the new guest is furry... or hairless, like me. Also, do you imagine that our new guest can swim—as I do?"

Alvin, the Friendly Alligator,
has a question for Wally:
"Do you suppose our new guest will be
mean or nice like me?" He adds,
"I always try to make new guests feel
welcomed and liked. After all,
I'm an alligator, so others always
assume I must be mean..."

Kimo, the Shy Koala, inquires of her neighbor, Gina, the Gentle Giraffe, "What do you predict? Will the new guest be fearless or shy, like me?"

Gina advises, "Don't worry, Kimo, I'm sure they will be a great neighbor! But I would love to know if the new guest is short or maybe tall, like me."

Henrietta, the Happy Hippo, is also interested in learning more. She muses, "Could the new guest be slender—or perhaps stout, like me?" She mentions to Lou, "I have room for our guest at my place if you don't have a home for them."

Lou responds that he is already preparing a new home in the zoo for the new guest.

That makes Henrietta even more eager to discover which animal would be getting the new neighbor!

Zelda, the Stylish Zebra, suggests to Rip the Black Rhino, "Is it possible that the new guest will have stripes?"

Rip replies, "We won't find out until they arrive."

Zelda remarks, "I love my beautiful black and white stripes. And it would be great if the guest had lovely stripes like me!"

Rip, the Black Rhino, ponders:
Am I the one who will be getting a new neighbor? And does the new guest run fast. . . or maybe walk slowly like me?

Ellie, the Playful Elephant,
asks Rip, "Do you expect they
will sleep all day—or play
at night like me?"

Rip answers Ellie,
"I wish I knew! Let's ask
them when they arrive!"

Now, Cali, the Colorful Chameleon, has also become very curious. She tells her roommate, Cassia, "It would be nice if the new guest could change its colors like us."

"I bet they can," declares Cassia. "If so, maybe they will become *our* new neighbor!"

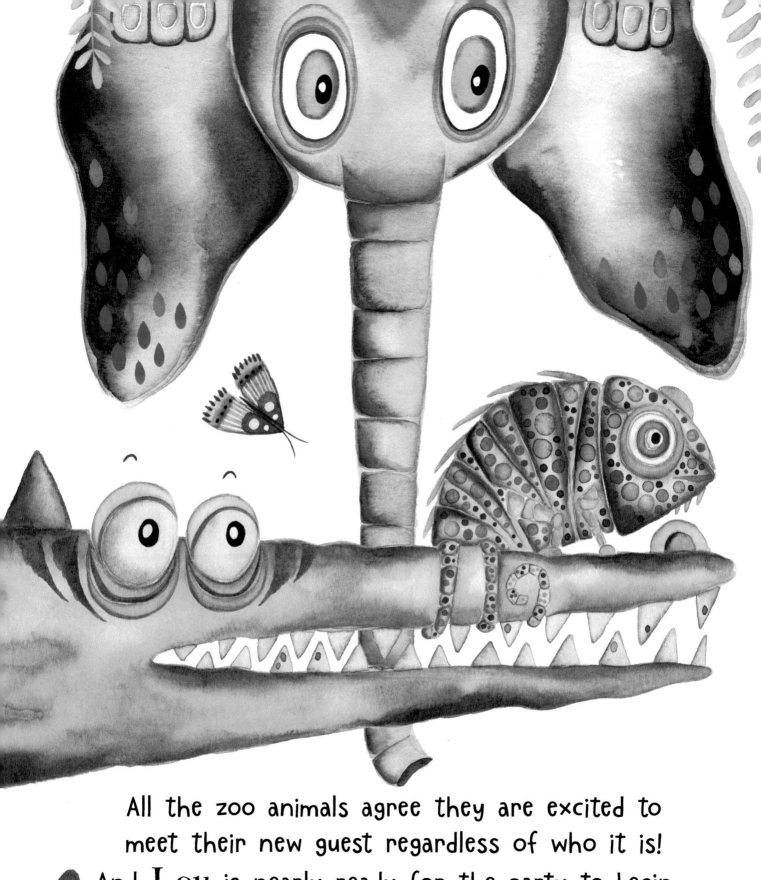

All the zoo animals agree they are excited to
meet their new guest regardless of who it is!
And Lou is nearly ready for the party to begin—
in honor of the new mystery guest!

The next day a truck arrives...and out comes **Martin the Mandrill**. He is the new guest!

Martin is very shy at first, entering the zoo with caution as he looks around.
As a newcomer, Martin has no idea what to expect from the other animals. He worries:
Will they think I'm mean or scary because of the way I look?

But right away,
Zelda observes admiringly,
"Look at him. He is
gorgeous! His fur has a
pattern that looks just
like my stripes!"

Kimo comments to
Mickey, "He looks scary
but has kind eyes."

Gina greets Martin and reassures him, "Don't be afraid. We have all come to welcome you, and we can't wait to become good friends!"

All the animals come out to greet and welcome Martin. Soon, he finds himself smiling and saying 'hi' to all his new neighbors. He's already relaxing and starting to believe he will love his new home!

Just then, Lou announces to all the animals, "Let the party begin—in honor of our new zoo neighbor, Martin!"

That night, just before falling asleep, Martin smiles and says to himself: "I think I'm going to like it here!"

Hi! "Martin is it?" My name is
Winston the Wise Owl.
Do you think Lou will let me
join the neighborhood too?

FUN FACTS

Alpaca

- There are only two breeds of alpacas, huacaya (wah-KI-ah) and suri (SOO-ree).

- They cannot live alone. Alpacas have strong herding instincts.

- Alpacas are vegetarian. A 125-lb. alpaca only eats 2-lbs. per day.

- Their diet mostly consists of grass, but can also include leaves, wood, bark, or stems.

- Alpacas do not have teeth in the top-front of their mouths. That's why they look like they have an adorable underbite!

- Their life span is 20 years.

Parrots

- They have four toes on each foot configured for maximum grip.

- Each foot has two toes in the front and two in the back.

- They eat fruit, seeds, nuts, and insects.

- Parrots taste food with the tops of their beaks.

Gorillas

- These animals can weigh close to four hundred ninety pounds and up to five feet five inches tall.

- They are one of the largest and most powerful living primates.

- Gorillas can eat all day long.

- They cozy up together at night and they live in family groups.

- A gorilla can live to be more than forty years old.

Monkeys

- They can live for ten to fifty years.
- While monkeys have tails, apes don't.
- Just like humans, monkeys have unique fingerprints.
- The largest monkey is the mandrill, which stands nearly three-and-a-half feet tall.

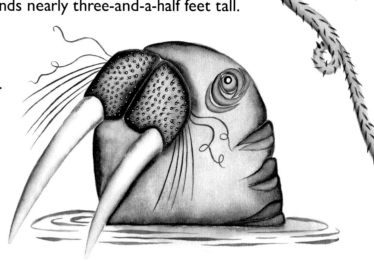

Walruses

- They can weigh up to fifteen hundred pounds.
- Walrus tusks can measure nearly three feet long & more than thirty-five inches.
- Thick layers of fat called blubber protect walruses from cold.
- Walruses can sleep in the water.
- They can live for up to forty years.

Alligators

- They are very social reptiles that gather in groups called 'congregations'.
- They can grow to eleven feet long and weigh up to a thousand pounds.
- Although they swim fast, alligators are clumsy on land.
- They primarily eat animals like fish, birds, frogs, and deer.
  - In the winter, they can go for months without eating.
    - Alligators in the wild can live for thirty to fifty years.

Koalas

- They are mammals native to Australia.
- They're often called Koala Bears but just like kangaroos, koalas are marsupials, not bears.
- Marsupial babies are carried in a pouch on their mother's bellies.
- Koalas are active mainly at night and live in eucalyptus forests.
- They eat gum leaves that are usually poisonous for other animals.

Giraffes

- They are the tallest mammals in the world.
- They stand up much of the time and sleep standing up.
- They're super-peaceful animals.
- The spots on giraffes' bodies are like fingerprints, No two are alike.
- They can live up to twenty-five years in the wild.

Hippo is short for hippopotamus

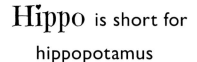

- This animal is the third-largest mammal.
- Hippos spend a lot of time in the water and resting in the water cools them down.
- They may look chubby, but they have no trouble outrunning a human.
- A male hippo is called a bull, and a female is called a calf.
- A group of hippos is known as a herd, pod, dale, or bloat.
- They eat mostly grass and can live up to forty-five years.

Zebras

- Their stripes are unique like fingerprints.
- Each of them sleeps standing up just like horses do.
- Zebras are part of the horse and donkey family.
- Sadly, these animals are an endangered species.

Elephants

- The largest living land animals so it's not surprising they can't jump.
- These animals spend up to sixteen hours per day, eating up to six hundred pounds in one day!
- They drink as much as fifty gallons of water daily.
- Elephants have great memories, using mud for sunscreen.
- They travel in herds and are afraid of bees.
- They can live up to seventy years.

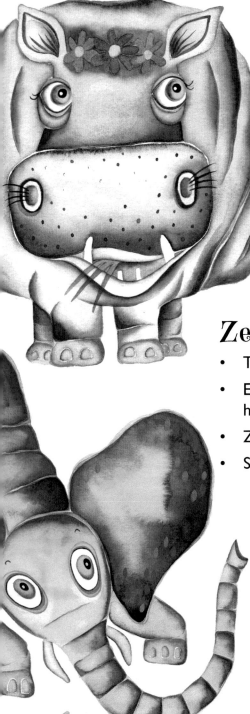

Rhinos

- There are at least five species of rhinos.
- Rhinos walk on their toes, there are three toes on each foot, with a soft pads to help cushion their enormous weight.
- Their giant horns contain the same stuff as human fingernails.
- They usually have two horns but sometimes have a third smaller posterior horn.
- Rhinos eat leaves from bushes and trees.
- They have poor vision and are easily frightened.

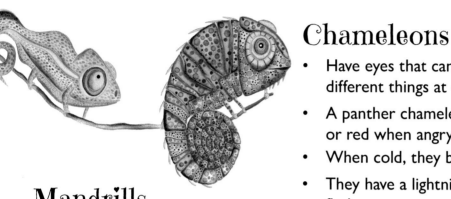

Chameleons

- Have eyes that can swivel to look at a few different things at once.
- A panther chameleon changes its color to yellow or red when angry.
- When cold, they become darker in color.
- They have a lightning-fast tongue that flashes out to snatch insects, stretching up to twenty-six times the length of their body.

Mandrills

- They're the largest of all the monkeys, and they are colorful.
- These animals spend most of their time on the ground.
- Each of them has a heavy body and a short tail.
- The color on a mandrill's face ranges from bright blue to violet, and along the bridge and end of the nose, it's scarlet.
- The long body fur ranges from olive to brown, while the small beard and the neck fur are yellow.
- Male mandrills are about three feet tall and weigh up to seventy-seven pounds. Females are much smaller.
- These animals live in troops and eat fruit roots, insects, and small reptiles.

Owl

- There are 200 different owl species.
- Owls are active at night (nocturnal).
- A group of owls is called a parliament.
- Most owls hunt insects, small mammals, and other birds.
- Owls have powerful talons (claws) which help them catch and kill prey.
- Owls have large eyes and flat face.
- Owls can turn their heads as much as 270 degrees.

JoAnn M. Dickinson moved to Southern
California at a young age, where she currently resides
with her husband. She is a wife, mother of one, and a
proud grandparent of two. She enjoys painting, drawing,
creating characters, and the writing process for her
children's books.

Author

2022 will be a busy year for JoAnn. She will launch 4
new children's books: Rylee The Young Rocketeer, John's
Camping Adventures, John's Camping Adventures At
Crab Run Beach, and Who's New At Lou's Zoo. All of
JoAnn's books are published by her publishing company,
Two Sweet Peas Publishing.

Lauren Sparks is a South African illustration artist
who finds much of her inspiration from nature's creatures,
magical forests, and the imaginations of children.

Illustrator

There is a uniquely playful style to Lauren's work, and she
tends to use rich colours with indistinctive backgrounds
for her dreamy characters; keeping her illustration
imaginative in nature.

Lauren's whimsical watercolour illustrations are an
invitation into an imaginary world in which we may
explore and re-unite with our own inner-child.

Thank you for your purchase!
If you enjoy this book, please go to Amazon.com: JoAnn M.
Dickinson: Books, Biography, Blog, Audiobooks, Kindle,
and click on Who's New At Lou's Zoo, and share your
thoughts about the book with others.

joannmdicksonauthor.com

Scan the QR code to sign up for my
newsletter and receive updates on events,
new releases, free downloads, and more!

JoAnn
Dickinson
Author

Made in the USA
Las Vegas, NV
16 May 2023

72159073R00026